D1546315

G.I.T.U.P.

The Audacity of Overcoming

Workbook

by Andrea M. Thompson

The author has recreated events, locales and conversations from her memories of them. In order to maintain their anonymity in some instances, she has changed the names of individuals and places. She may have also changed some identifying characteristics and details such as physical properties, occupations and places of residence.

Most Scriptures are derived from the public domain version of the King James Version of *The Holy Bible*. Isaiah 54:11-17 has been taken from *THE MESSAGE*. Copyright © 1993, 1994, 1995, 1996, 2000, 2001, 2002. Used by permission of NavPress Publishing Group. Quotations have been sourced and attributed to the best of the author's knowledge.

Quantity Sales Ordering Information: Special discounts are available on quantity purchases by corporations, associations, and others. For details, contact the author at this address:

c/o A.M. Thompson Enterprises, LLC

1440 W. Taylor Street #1725

Chicago, IL 60607

Editor & Graphic Designer: Renée Purdie
ISBN: 979-8-9873707-0-4

Dedication

Before I formed thee in the belly I knew thee; and before thou camest forth out of the womb I sanctified thee, and I ordained thee a prophet unto the nations.
JEREMIAH 1:5

Contents

INTRODUCTION _____ 1

CHAPTER 1 PURPOSE ROOTED IN PAIN _____ 2

CHAPTER 2 THE GIFT IN THE GAB _____ 7

CHAPTER 3 AT GUNPOINT: UNCOVERED YET KEPT _____13

CHAPTER 4 THE LONGEST FLIGHT HOME _____16

CHAPTER 5 DEFERRED DREAMS & WOODEN NICKELS ___20

CHAPTER 6 FAITH UNDER FIRE _____25

CHAPTER 7 OVERCOMING INJUSTICE _____33

CHAPTER 8 YOUR AUDACIOUS STORY _____37

CHAPTER 9 THE AUDACITY OF SAVING GRACE _____43

CHAPTER 10 CONCLUDING THOUGHTS_____48

JOURNEY NOTES _____53

ABOUT THE AUTHOR _____55

WAYS TO BE AUDACIOUS _____57

RESOURCES & CONNECTIONS GUIDE _____58

DISCUSSION QUESTIONS _____60

SPACE FOR ADDITIONAL NOTES _____62

Introduction

This workbook was created to accompany the book, G.I.T.U.P. The Audacity of Overcoming. It is best used in tandem with it, but it also contains some of the best excerpts, affirmations and quotes from the book. It also contains prompts and writing space for you to document your own audacious journey.

Crisis is the perfect opportunity for a blessing to show up more powerfully than ever if we just endure. That is the audacity of overcoming.

Rest when you need to be restored.

Recharge when you're running low.

But <u>always</u> remain resilient!

Chapter 1

Purpose Rooted In Pain

The enemy will always send a terrorist alert when you are close to your destiny.

—Bishop T.D. Jakes

Sometimes you are your own terrorist. Self-sabotage is real and the limiting thoughts that are rooted in a painful past based on the limiting thoughts of others can thwart your progress to success.

Connection Clue

What things did you believe about yourself that you had to dispel and think about differently in order to create different outcomes?

Are there some people in your close circle who could possibly pose major liabilities (thwarting your path to success) if they don't change, or you don't eliminate them from your inner circle? What attributes are you soaking up from them being close to you?

What subpar treatment are you tolerating? What relationships are you maintaining where your presence is being tolerated and not necessarily appreciated?

Is there a terrorist alert that you need to address in order to operate with keen discernment and peace? This could be a toxic relationship, an unhealthy addiction, or a self-limiting thought that you affirm by giving it credence.

What attributes does your circle need to reflect to support where you are going in your higher destiny and goals? Assess your current circle in comparison to what you need to give and receive from your closest connections. Some relationships may have to change. Others may become non-existent. That's okay, and it may not be either person's fault. It's just a new step towards your destiny.

> "I wanted to surround myself with the kind of people who could help me turn my life around; people whom I could rub up against like iron and be sharpened."—Eric "ET" Thomas

Attributes of your current circle	Attributes of your desired circle

I am connected to amazing people who genuinely want to see me win. I am attracting mutually beneficial relationships. I am realigning or removing connections that are self-serving, toxic or counterproductive. My crew is growing with me, and we are dynamic, loyal and full of promise.

Chapter 2

The Gift in the Gab

A man's gift maketh room for him,
and bringeth him before great men.
Proverbs 18:16

God created us with purpose and with that He planted in us seeds in the form of gifts. Those gifts may not be flourishing right now because of inattention or circumstances, but a surefire way to start to release them is to focus on identifying them.

> "We all go through pain; get a reward for it."
>
> —Eric "ET" Thomas

What special gifts, talents or passions has the Lord equipped you with on this journey? They may well be connected to your pain points.

What is something that you have been struggling with, something that is painful and perhaps hindering you from accomplishing your goals and having a better quality of life? What teachable moments have you had during your valley moments?

Reflect on what measures you took to push through, and what skills you used to navigate the difficulty of that situation. Maybe you developed a new skill or learned more about yourself.

Your first concern might not be writing to document a challenge while you're working to overcome it, but I can tell you this for sure, if you write even when it hurts the most, you not only put the pain on the paper but you leave a "gladiator's guide" that helps others know that they can GITUP too. Turn the inspiration to energy!

Connecting the dots

What would the breakthrough story of your life look like? Go further: what would it FEEL like? Sketch it out. Write the story. Record yourself speaking it. You often have to envision it before you can achieve it. Write it and make it plain.

_____

_____

_____

_____

_____

_____

_____

_____

_____

_____

_____

_____

_____

_____

_____

_____

_____

_____

_____

_____

_____

_____

_____

_____

_____

_____

_____

_____

_____

_____

Audacity Affirmation

I will use my voice powerfully, declaring that I am going to use all of my gifts, treasures and talents boldly and impactfully. I won't be silenced, if I choose to speak. But even when silent, my silence can make a statement.

Chapter 3

At Gunpoint:
Uncovered Yet Kept

The LORD is nigh unto them that
are of a broken heart; and saveth
such as be of a contrite spirit.
Psalm 34:18

Have you been through a lifesaving moment, or
something life-altering that showed you the reality
you were living was not the reality you envisioned?
Maybe you're living it now.

What do you need to change? What steps do you need
to take?

Ironically, it took a near-death experience to realize staying in a toxic relationship was actually already killing me, word by word, and day by day. It was killing my self-esteem, my energy and my dreams. I'm so thankful I made it out alive with the seeds to thrive by the grace of God.

Physical death is not the only death we can endure. Sometimes people or circumstances can kill our joy, motivation, dreams and hopes. Pray for discernment and start listing areas where you need to have restoration.

_____

_____

_____

_____

_____

_____

_____

_____

_____

_____

Audacity Affirmation

I will love like I've never been hurt. I will have the courage to trust again and let down my guard in God's perfect timing. God does all things well and He loves best. I am love and I am loved.

Chapter 4

The Longest Flight Home

"I have walked that long road to freedom. I have tried not to falter; I have made missteps along the way. But I have discovered the secret that after climbing a great hill, one only finds that there are many more hills to climb. I have taken a moment here to rest, to steal a view of the glorious vista that surrounds me, to look back on the distance I have come. But I can only rest for a minute, for with freedom come responsibilities, and I dare not linger, for my long walk is not ended."

—Nelson Mandela

Sometimes it takes a long time to get you back to where you wanted to go in the first place. You may have decided to follow a career path because of what your parents wanted you to do. You may have decided not to go to Paris to follow your dream of being an artist. You may be feeling that your special talent for creating cakes is just a little hobby when you could be creating cakes for celebrities like Oprah. Dust off those dreams and you may well discover a whole new you, the one ignited by passion and purpose.

Write down some dreams and goals you have been afraid to think about because you never thought you'd achieve them.

How have you been forced to affirm yourself even when society invalidates you?

_____

_____

_____

_____

_____

_____

_____

_____

_____

_____

_____

_____

You are the first to know your thoughts. What you think of yourself matters. How you talk to yourself matters. Let me make it crystal clear: YOU MATTER, NO MATTER WHAT THEY SAY. You matter, even when they don't say you do. Be kind to yourself. The world won't always embrace you. In fact, most times we will have to stand strong and firm in the face of formidable opponents and longstanding systems meant for our demise.

Arrogance is not the same as confidence. We can be proud, yet humble. Jesse Jackson's mantra "keep hope alive" translated to me as "keep hope from dying." Sometimes hope barely has a pulse. You might fall low, but do not faint in welldoing. God sees you and He sees the best in you. You are the apple of His eye and His greatest creation. We are descendants of royalty and have an inheritance.

Audacity Affirmation

I will stay hopeful by being a beacon of light that shines in dark places. Even when it's not a popular thing to do, I will stand up for what is right and righteous, armed with the breastplate of truth as my primary weapon against the hands of the enemy. I will advocate for change, advocate for the disadvantaged, and be a voice for the voiceless. In a small step or a large leap, I will help to create the change we all need to see.

Chapter 5

Deferred Dreams &
Wooden Nickels

And we know that all things work together for good to
them that love God, to them who are the called
according to his purpose.
Romans 8:28

What are some adverse circumstances that the Lord
worked out for your good?

_____

_____

_____

_____

_____

_____

_____

_____

_____

How have you been forced to affirm yourself even when society invalidates you?

_____

_____

_____

_____

_____

_____

_____

_____

_____

_____

Reflecting on my journey, I see great parallels to the story of Noah. He was asked to build an ark when at that time there had never been rain!

And I Daniel alone saw the vision: for the men that were with me saw not the vision; but a great quaking fell upon them, so that they fled to hide themselves.
Daniel 10:7

Have you harbored resentment for a situation that you thought you should have responded to differently? Maybe in the moment you couldn't bring yourself to respond like you thought you would?

Have you had to delay what you thought was an imperative part of God's plan for your life? How could that delay actually serve as preparation? Reflect on the ways in which it could actually be a way to better position yourself even more powerfully!

I resist the urge to do things in my own timing and surrender to God's timing, knowing that His plan and foresight are much greater than my own. He is the supreme orchestrator of time and works all things together for my good. Even delays are refining me, not defying or defining me. I forgive myself for not taking action in times when the crisis caused me to freeze. I am strong when I am still. I am strong when I activate. I will further develop my gifts and activate my growth process by feeding my mind, body and spirit with things that will nurture my ability to overcome!

Chapter 6

Faith Under Fire

Now faith is the substance of things hoped for,
the evidence of things not seen.
Hebrews 11:1

> "I've had the opportunity to lose everything twice. In each situation, all I could do was turn to God. God allowed me to come back, and the comeback was more significant and more substantial than any loss could have ever been. God has sustained me. God has allowed me to grow amid challenges. God spoke to my spirit, which allowed me to change my mind and pivot. So I am clear, God is the Ultimate Plug!"
>
> —Marki Lemons-Ryhal

 ow can losing everything be an opportunity? You have to change your perspective to change your position!

Have you ever had a setback that set you up for a comeback? Describe it as it may inspire someone else to push through something that they feel is impossible to deal with.

And Jesus said unto them, Because of your unbelief: for verily I say unto you, If ye have faith as a grain of mustard seed, ye shall say unto this mountain, Remove hence to yonder place; and it shall remove; and nothing shall be impossible unto you.
Matthew 17:20

When was the last time you were fully willing to go through the fire for a set period of time to cause an infinite outpouring of blessings? It's a selfless sacrifice. You see, the blessings are often not just for you.

In some parts of the world there are fire-activated seeds, one being the seeds of the eucalyptus. Their seeds can only open after they have physically gone through a fire and that is the only way they can reproduce and produce! You see to activate something and set it in motion, there has to be a catalyst. The thing you see as a crisis could actually be the catalyst that leads to your blessing!

Is there a situation in your life that you can use as a catalyst for your NEXT?

You will lose some things along the way, material items, close friends, and maybe even some family too. Sometimes you lose, not in the physical, as the thing is still present but has no presence. But in all thy losing, know that God can and will turn the loss into a gain. Whatever you may lose along the way, don't harden your heart. Forgive those who kicked you while you were down. They may be undeserving of your forgiveness according to your feelings and their transgressions, but you deserve to live as if you've never ever been hurt.

Who do you need to forgive in order to lighten your load so you can FLY? That can often include yourself.

So whatever you lose along the way, don't lose your faith. It is the substance of things unseen and the light in the tunnel when darkness is unveiled all around you. It is in darkness where the seed first takes root. It is also in darkness that God's light shines brightest. Where is the light in your dark situation? How do you expand that light?

Stay connected to the source and ask Him (in His infinite wisdom) to give you increased discernment and wisdom while orchestrating a village of people who will make contact with you and use their light to illuminate yours. This is how faith in action starts to serve as a catalyst for things to line up in a powerful way. As you experience a shift to elevate you, you will not only change your circumstances. but you'll change your life.

Connection Clue Bonus

What is something that you have been struggling with—something that is painful, but going through it gave you perspective? What teachable moments, solutions, and breakthrough stories can help you navigate other challenges as well as impacting and inspiring others?

Audacity Affirmation

Everything I need is within my reach. If I don't possess it within me, I am attracting it to me by operation of my gifts in service to others. No good thing will be withheld from me. The financial means to achieve my goals is coming to me as if I am magnetically charged, because I am AUDACIOUS!

Chapter 7

Overcoming Injustice

Blessed is the man that endureth temptation: for when
he is tried, he shall receive the crown of life, which the
Lord hath promised to them that love him.
James 1:12

"I'm no longer accepting the things I cannot
change ... I'm changing the things I cannot
accept."—Dr. Angela Davis

Is there a particular injustice or situation
you've noticed? Think of some ways you can be an
agent for change.

You have to watch where you place people in your auditorium because everybody isn't equipped to have a front row seat. Think about the flight attendant's announcement about the emergency row. "If you are not able or willing to perform the tasks associated with the position in the event of an emergency, please alert an attendant so that she can reseat you."

Who do you need to reseat? Indeed, you may actually need for some people to be deplaned. Write it down to make it plain (or plane)!

Reseat	Deplane

A false witness shall not be unpunished,
and he that speaketh lies shall not escape.
Proverbs 19:5

A lil' old lady once told me, "I don't wanna keep up
no mess and I don't mean to bother nobody, but I
know you got to stand for something or you'll fall for
anything. Stand firm on the buckle of truth and don't
take no wooden nickels." Amen! We gotta press on,
and get in good trouble. We gotta fight the good fight
and keep the faith, especially in the midst of
overcoming injustice. In short, we must be
audacious!

Connection Clue

Speaking out can make you a target. Has there been
a time when you've had to make a difficult choice,
keeping the greater good in mind?

How have you continued to love and forgive in spite of the hurt and hate?

_____
_____
_____
_____
_____
_____
_____
_____
_____
_____
_____

Chapter 8

Your Audacious Story

> I think my inner child wants to take over the world.—Mark Foster

What does your inner child want to do?

Reflect on a time that God pulled you out of a crowd and had you forego the standard procedure for advancement and preferential treatment not based on your own merit but His favor and grace—a time where you knew without a shadow of a doubt that it was Him.

Once you recall that moment, write down three ways He brought you through and/or helped you be in an even better position after the struggle. What lessons about faith and resilience can you glean from that experience?

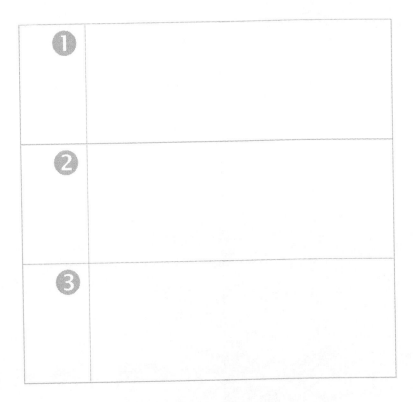

You have your own AUDACIOUS story to draw from. If you are compelled to share your story or dive deeper into this topic area, please join us in our Facebook group: bit.ly/GITUPOnFacebook

Start sketching out your story here. Your journey begins with the first word.

Audacity Affirmation

What is your life motto?

Audacity Affirmation

What's your Audacity Theme Song?

Chapter 9

The Audacity of Saving Grace

If anyone attacks you,

don't for a moment suppose that I sent them,

And if any should attack,

nothing will come of it.

I create the blacksmith

who fires up his forge

and makes a weapon designed to kill.

I also create the destroyer—

but no weapon that can hurt you has ever been
forged.

Any accuser who takes you to court

will be dismissed as a liar.

This is what God's servants can expect.

I'll see to it that everything works out for the best."

Wickedness in high places is difficult to fight against, yet there are some of us equipped and called to the task of eradicating bias, dispelling myths and educating people to do the same when they face similar situations.

What battle are you avoiding because of its difficulty? How are you educating yourself on the preparation required to fight the good fight with grace and effectiveness? You're not ranting and you are not alone. You may need to reposition your message and speak to the right people in decision-making positions.

I am equipped to fight against injustice because I survived the things they used to try to break me. My voice and the courage to speak out properly equips me because as Dr. Martin Luther King, Jr. reminded us "an injustice anywhere is a threat to justice everywhere." We have to be willing to get into good trouble in order to fight the good and very necessary fight for fairness and equality. I run with the strength that my ancestors walked with!

Chapter 10

Concluding Thoughts: The Next Phase

And be not conformed to this world: but be ye transformed by the renewing of your mind, that ye may prove what is that good, and acceptable, and perfect, will of God.
Romans 12:2

Audacity is defined in the dictionary as a willingness to take bold risks. I'll add to that definition having the bravery to do something that could offend others or upset the enemy's plans. *The Audacity of Overcoming* is the resiliency spirit of the underdog against formidable obstacles. There is a particular persistence, a brazen boldness, and an unrelenting force. It is a full faith walk rooted in certainty and blessed assurance. It is also a costly confirmation that hope will bring you out that much better.

There is an art to pressing forward and doing so with such grace that your ability to withstand becomes a blueprint of overcoming to inspire others to also grow and glow through gracefully. The pressure process births a diamond. The crushing of the olive produces the oil. But yes, the oil costs; your pain is the purchase price. Pay your dues; learn the lessons and expect the blessing.

The oil will protect your anointing and lead to your reward. Remember the eucalyptus seed has to germinate after literally being under fire. Often there is a forcing that takes place to push and catapult us. It is uncomfortable. It is stretching. I've been realigned, repositioned, reassigned and rearranged, but I've also been restored amidst chaos, confusion and turmoil. God can use it all. Not a hurricane, a crisis, depression, nor an intermittent pandemic can counter God's plan. Even those adversities can be used for His perfect purpose. Willingly accept His will, leaning not to your own understanding, but fully trusting that He sees your struggle and knows your midnight cry.

In what areas do you need to slow down and how can you use your connections in other areas where you need to act expeditiously?

You can't change the world and your circumstances without the one that formed the world and made you. Stay connected, especially in a storm. God is a guide, a resource, a surge protector and gives you elevator lift!

Ground Transportation

Sometimes we want to fly, but we only have the funds for Greyhound. Sometimes we don't appreciate that even though flying gets us there faster, at least we are moving on the Greyhound. The key though is to use that extra time wisely. If you have a 40-hour train trip, you could have written most of a book. Reputedly, John Boyne wrote *The Boy in the Striped Pajamas* in two and a half days.

Takeoff: I See the Victory

The proper weight to take off requires a release. The pressure produces the elements for lift. The lift is required to truly soar. Sometimes you're at the bus station waiting for a delayed bus when your calling requires you to be at the airport for an on-time departure!

Unexpected Turbulence

Don't lose focus or get nervous when you hear the PSA warning you of unexpected turbulence. Don't turn around no matter what anyone says. If you knew how close you were, you would put on earbuds and tune in completely to what He is saying to you.

Every adversity that you went through lines up so perfectly that you knew He was doing it for you all along and that He had your overcoming in mind. He did it for you! You can't even reconcile how to tell somebody what He did and just how awesome and amazing it was. God gave me something to grow with and something to sow with. What He has for me is so much more than my plan could ever be.

While attending the Rolling Out Ride Conference, who are you rolling out with? Who are you riding with? Remember that you cannot take everyone on the journey with you. You cannot mistake a friend for an enemy. There's too much riding on your success.

Connecting Flights

The road to success and your life destiny is very often not linear. It is full of delays, re-routes and both scheduled and unscheduled stops. Connections are good, but God is navigating the connections. It is His plans unfolding that is sending the help. I give Him the honor while thanking the people that He sent.

There a lot of things, people, organizations, memberships and circles you can be connected to, but the best connection you can ever have is with your Creator. There will be times when the people you've known for decades, or maybe even since birth, won't understand you. To be honest, they may start to seem and sound strange to you too. Don't become so distracted in the layover season that you miss your connection flight.

Who is powerful enough to prolong your struggle and sabotage your success? You cannot afford to risk it all for someone who is prone to risk and consumed with consistency of problems, yet offers few solutions. Get around people who are positioned to help you excel in a powerful way. They will not always be people you expected. In fact, it may be people you least expected to have anything to even bless you with, but when God chooses to bless you in a way that only He can, things align in a powerful way. Then you have to walk boldly and embody the light when you move through dark spaces.

Baggage Claim and Extra Baggage

You're almost there! Then you go to a carousel to claim your baggage. Hopefully, you pack more strategically than I used to so that you don't overpack. However, if you are like me, you may tend to carry the weight of things you hold on to unnecessarily on the journey. What extra baggage are you carrying?

What role did you play in adverse situations? I think we often process best by moving on past the hurt and unburdening ourselves of all that extra weight. Better still, let me carry on instead and check this baggage.

Landing the Plane

God has the perfect purpose in everything! The egg met the sperm at the ideal time to create you. The Ultimate Plug plugged you to win the race, but you have to stay connected to get an energy supply. There are people running around looking for a lil' juice. Different chargers charge your phone at different speeds. Make sure you're connected to The Source because God Is The Ultimate Plug to give you The Audacity of Overcoming!

JOURNEY NOTES

✈ Check your passenger travel list.
✈ The critical phases of flight are takeoff and landing.
✈ Descent comes before final approach.
✈ In the unlikely event of an emergency, secure yourself first.

About the Author

Andrea is an ambitious mother, business owner, native Chicagoan, and philanthropist who diligently works to build a legacy brand to secure her son's future while creating and supporting initiatives that contribute to domestic violence prevention, senior story sharing, as well as economic and youth empowerment. Her current outreach includes fundraising scholarships for students attending HBCUs through the Audacious Midwest To South Scholarship / EBJV Memorial Foundation.

Through Live In The Content Kitchen™, Andrea candidly interviews professionals and everyday extraordinary people over conversations, cocktails and cuisine. When she isn't speaking or working, she enjoys cooking, traveling, and creating new opportunities and adventures for clients and colleagues. Andrea is primarily based in Chicago, but enjoys taking her talents cross-country and is looking forward to taking *The Audacity of Overcoming* international.

Follow Andrea's Audacious Adventures by connecting with the GITUP Movement online.

www.theaudacityofovercoming.com

IG: @AndreaIsThePlug

TikTok: @AndreaIsThePlug

FB: bit.ly/GITUPOnFacebook

Ways To Be Audacious

Audacious Midwest To South Scholarship /
EBJV Memorial Foundation

**For in-kind support or matching donation
pledges, please email us at
connect@theaudacityofovercoming.com.**

Resources & Connections Guide: Pass the Plug

For continued resources and membership opportunities for exclusive offerings, join the GITUP FB community at: bit.ly/GITUPOnFacebook.

There will be podcast announcements and exclusive interviews with audacious leaders in mental health, business and youth empowerment arenas.

We will be interviewing mindset coaches, singers, beauty professionals and other amazing global-minded power brokers.

Sharing Your Story

Marketing Your Brand Story
Andrea M. Thompson, Courageous Content Creator
Email: connect@theaudacityofovercoming.com

Personal/Professional Development

Dr. Jeanne Porter King

www.jeanneporterking.com

Health and Wellness

Follow Live In The Content Kitchen™ Facebook page!

https://www.facebook.com/ContentInTheKitchen

Get a taste for this foodie's movement by visiting the recipes in the back of this book.

Discussion Questions

1. What does audacity mean to you? Share your answers in our Facebook group or tag us on social media with #TheAudacityofOvercoming. Include a selfie with your copy of the book and be placed in a competition to receive The Audacity of Overcoming (TAoO) merchandise!

2. How would you describe "The Audacity of Overcoming" (not the book, but we welcome a review), but for this question we mean what does it mean and look like? What are the characteristics of "The Audacity of Overcoming"?

3. Does Michelle Obama's famous quote "When They Go Low, We Go High" sometimes make you feel that taking the high road can allow undeserving people to get the best of you as we are told to turn the other cheek?

4. How do we balance the aforementioned with knowing that vengeance belongs to the Lord, while also balancing holding ourselves and others accountable?

5. What are some takeaways on the importance of healthy daddy/daughter/mommy/son relationships? What are some key things that are important for fathers and mothers to know?

6. What are four core values/characteristics that contribute to being relentless and resilient in the pursuit of greatness and success?

7. What things did you perceive to be flaws in your younger years that you now see as perfect imperfections that you are now able to embrace as unique parts of yourself?

8. Parenting: Being a Single mother and trying to co-parent can be challenging, yet very rewarding. Co-parenting can further complicate healthy parenting. What are some of the key things that you have observed or implemented and have found to be useful and effective in instilling values in children, even when the parents are raising the children separately? What is some solid advice that you have found to be useful, particularly when it comes to raising Black young men?

9. Reflect on a time when you had to forgive someone who inflicted a great deal of heartache, shame and hurt. In hindsight, how did forgiving (in spite of whether or not they deserved it) help you to get free?

10. Injustice and discrimination are sometimes the most difficult atrocities to battle. The devastation of bias chips away at your soul. Many of us have witnessed firsthand or via societal exposure death and disappointment at the hands of people and systems sworn in and in position to serve and protect. How has the trauma of bias, discrimination, and injustice affected you and/or those you love? What have been some positive steps towards healing that you have found to be effective?

Bonus Questions

7AoO   Do you believe that the author Ms. Andrea Thompson could have created the same book if she was born anywhere besides the southside of Chicago? What do you feel growing up there imparted to her?

7AoO   What are the biggest takeaways you have from reading *The Audacity of Overcoming*?

Notes

Notes

Notes